My Granny is a QUEEN

Written by
Madeleine Cook

Illustrated by
Rebecca Ashdown

 **OXFORD**
UNIVERSITY PRESS

My Granny is a QUEEN

or Brenda   Mama Mugglestone

Delia   Ellen   Gladys

Helen   Margaret

Nancy

Original concept and
words by Clare Whitston
and Gillian Sore.

OXFORD
UNIVERSITY PRESS

Oxford is a registered trademark
of Oxford University Press in the UK
and certain other countries

Text © Oxford University Press 2022
Illustrations © Rebecca Ashdown 2022

British Library Cataloguing
in Publication Data

Data available

ISBN: 978-0-19-278410-0

Printed in the UK

www.oup.com

and ALL grannies everywhere!

My granny is a **QUEEN**.

Today is a very important day because she is paying us a royal visit.

We line up to greet her and **Curtsy** as she walks down the red carpet.

Sometimes a **QUEEN** has a royal pet, and my nana has two.

They are called

Lord Stinkerton

and

Lady Battenberg the Third.

pooff!

They are **very** classy, as you would expect royal dogs to be.

They **almost** never misbehave.

My nonna is a QUEEN.

For important queenly duties, she wears the precious royal jewels.

Sometimes, if I am VERY lucky, she lets me try them on.

My oma has a royal carriage.
We all pile in—
    my brothers,
        my sister
            and me—

and take a stately drive into town.

My bibi is a **QUEEN**, and so together we go to

GRAND
OPENINGS,

DELIGHTFUL
BALLS,

and all sorts of

FABULOUS
EVENTS.

Well-wishers line the streets
cheering
because they are so excited to see a QUEEN.

Our grandma always makes time to stop
and talk or to give a royal wave.

My nai nai is a QUEEN.

Giving **important
speeches**
is something
every queen
must do.

You can do it!

When someone has done something very brave, a QUEEN
will give them a special award to say

well done.

It is a great honour to receive an award from my gran.

My nanny
is a **QUEEN**.

She lives in a
faraway castle.

We speak to her from our sofa, sharing all our important news.

My baba is a QUEEN.

When we get home after a long day,
Baba takes a seat on the royal throne
and we bring her the
royal slippers.

When I am ready for bed, my nani tells me great stories of all the QUEENS that came before her.

They sound **brave** and **strong** and funny.

Just like her.

My abuela is a QUEEN, which is why she has a crown.

My granny

nana

nonna

oma

bibi

grandma

nai nai

gran

nanny

baba

nani

abuela

is a **QUEEN.**

QUEENS do like a party.
Granny do too!

My granny might not be **THE** queen,
but she'll always be a **QUEEN** to me!